SAILOR JACK SERIES

SAILOR JACK AND HOMER POTS

SAILOR JACK AND EDDY

SAILOR JACK

SAILOR JACK AND BLUEBELL'S DIVE

SAILOR JACK AND BLUEBELL

SAILOR JACK AND THE JET PLANE

SAILOR JACK AND THE BALL GAME

SAILOR JACK'S NEW FRIEND

SAILOR JACK AND THE TARGET SHIP

SAILOR JACK GOES NORTH

SAILOR JACK

by Selma and Jack Wassermann

pictures by Don Loehle

Benefic Press   Chicago

Publishing Division of Beckley-Cardy Company

CONTENTS

Library of Congress
Number 60-6590

Sailor Jack and Bluebell

This is Sailor Jack.

Sailor Jack works on a ship.

This is Bluebell.
Bluebell likes the ship.
Bluebell can help Jack.

Jack works here.

"Come, Bluebell," said Jack.

"You can help."

"Help! Help!"
said Bluebell.

The sailors ran to Jack.

"Here we come!" they said.

"We will help!"

"I wanted Bluebell to help,"
said Jack.

"Bluebell did not help.
She did not work."

The sailors said,
"Bluebell likes
to play."
They laughed
at Bluebell.

"Bluebell
can not
play here.
Go away,
Bluebell,"
said Jack.

Where Is Bluebell?

Then Bluebell
went away.
She did not
want Jack
to find her.

Bluebell looked.

She saw Jack.

She saw the sailors.

They did not see Bluebell.

"Look! Look!" said a sailor.
"Work fast!"
Jack said, "This is not good!"

The sailors worked and worked.
Jack worked, too.

Something did not look good.
Bluebell did not see it.

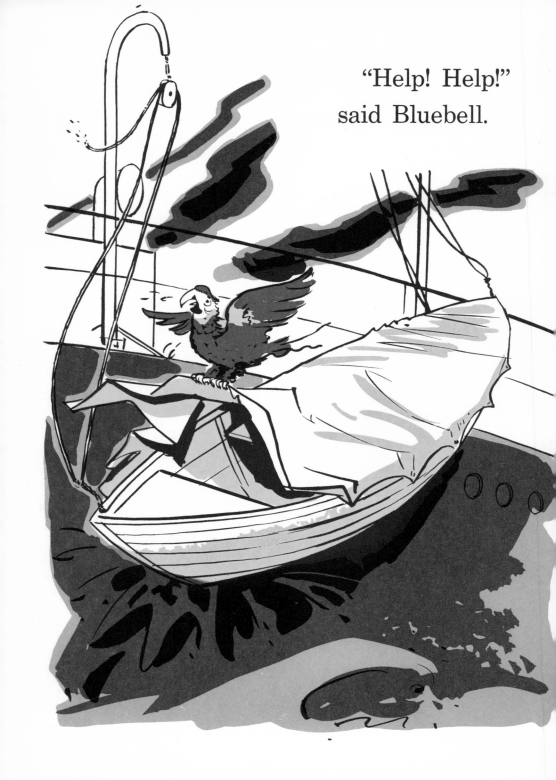

"Help! Help!"
said Bluebell.

Jack Helps Bluebell

"Bluebell!" said Jack.

Sailor Jack ran to look for Bluebell.
"Bluebell! Bluebell!" Jack said.
"Where are you?"

Then Jack
saw Bluebell.
"I will come
to you," he said.
"Bluebell, I will
help you!"

SPLASH!

Down went Jack.

Down went Bluebell.

Away they went!

Jack said, "Now we will go.
We will go to the ship."
Jack looked.
"Where is the ship?" he said.
"I can not see the ship."

Sailor Jack
looked and looked.

He did not
see the ship.

Then Jack said,
"Ships will come.

A ship will come
to help."

Help Comes

Jack looked for a ship.

Bluebell said, "Aaak!"

Away went Bluebell.

"Bluebell, come here!" said Jack.

Bluebell went on.

Bluebell went down.
"What is it?" Jack said.
"What did you see, Bluebell?"
Jack went to Bluebell.

"Aaak! Aaak!" said Bluebell.

Jack said, "Bluebell!

You did find something good.

This is a submarine.

A submarine is here!"

Bluebell looked.
She saw the
submarine captain.
   The captain said,
"I see something!
   Up! Up!" he said
to the sailors.
   "I want
the submarine
to go up."

Up went the submarine.
Up went Jack and Bluebell!
"Look! Look!" said Jack.
"We are on the submarine.
Here come the sailors!"

"Come!" said the sailors.

They went down in the submarine.

A Submarine Dive

Jack went to the captain.

The captain said, "This submarine is the U. S. S. SHARK.

It is a fast atomic submarine.

You will come with the SHARK.

Then you will go to the ship you worked on."

Jack went with the sailors.

He saw the SHARK.

"This is a good ship," said Jack.

"Good ship!" said Bluebell.

The sailors laughed at Bluebell.

They liked Bluebell.

"Dive!" said the captain.

"Dive!" said the sailor.

"Dive!" said Bluebell.

The SHARK went down fast.

Then Bluebell said, "Aaaaaak!"
Away she went.
"Come here, Bluebell!" said Jack.
Bluebell did not come.

"What is this?"
said the captain.

"It is the dive,"
said Jack.

"Dives are new
for Bluebell."

The captain said,
"I did not like
what Bluebell did."
Jack said,
"I will look
for her."

Jack looked
and looked.

He did not
find Bluebell.

Jack said,
"Where will I
look now?"

The captain
wanted something.
He said,
"Here it is.
I want this."

34

Then something
jumped up fast.
Bluebell jumped
at the captain!
Bluebell said,
"Dive! Dive!"

The captain looked at Bluebell.
Then he said, "Come, Jack.
Bluebell is here."

Bluebell went with Jack.
Jack said, "Be good, Bluebell.
I want to work on the SHARK.
You will have to be good.
The captain will not want me.
He did not like what you did."

Jack Works

The sailors
did work
on the SHARK.

Jack saw
the work.

He liked the
work here.

Then Jack worked, too.

He did atomic submarine work.

The sailors said,
"We like Jack.
We like Bluebell.
We want Jack to work here."

The captain saw Jack work, too.
He said, "You are a good sailor.
I want you on this atomic ship."

"Good! Good!" said Jack.
"What a good day for me!
I like this new atomic submarine."

The captain said, "And Bluebell.
Will she like the SHARK?
Submarines have to dive.
Will she be good?"

"She will be
good," Jack said.
"You will see.
Bluebell likes
to dive now."

"Dive! Dive!"
said Bluebell.
The captain
laughed at her.
"Dive!" he said
to the sailors.

Down went
the SHARK!

Away went Bluebell.

Bluebell jumped up here.
"Good dive!" said Bluebell.
"Good dive!"

VOCABULARY

The total vocabulary of this book is 62 words, excluding proper names. The 44 words in roman type should be familiar to children reading at preprimer level. The 17 words above preprimer level are shown in italic type. The numbers indicate the pages on which the words first appear.

a 5
and 5
are 17
at 10
atomic 28
away 10

be 37

can 6
captain 25
come 7

did 9
dive 28
down 19

fast 13
find 11
for 17

go 10
good 13

have 37
he 18
help 6

her 11
here 7

I 9
in 27
is 5
it 23

jumped 35

laughed 10
likes 6
looked 12

me 37

new 32
not 9
now 20

on 5

play 10

ran 8

said 7
sailors 8
saw 12

see 12
she 11
ship 5
something 15
submarine 24

the 6
then 11
they 8
this 5
to 8
too 14

up 25

wanted 9
we 8
went 11
what 23
where 11
will 8
with 29
works 5

you 7